CONTENTS

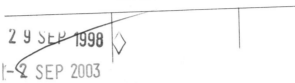
SECTION ONE: INTRODUCTION

SECTION TWO: DEFINING & ASSESSING NEEDS

SECTION THREE: SUPPORTING CPD

CONTENTS

SECTION ONE: INTRODUCTION

1.   Foreword

As this Guide indicates, the professional institutions in construction have for a very long time been providing a variety of services and activities to enable their members to keep up-to-date and continue learning throughout their careers.

Since the early '70s a number have been developing formal policies concerning what has come to be called continuing professional development (CPD) — motivating and assisting members to improve and broaden knowledge, skills and attitudes bearing in mind that CPD is the means to an end, the end being improved performance.

The CPD in Construction Group has been the focus for much of this development.

An essential but sometimes absent partner in the process has been the organisation — by which we mean companies, practices and the relevant departments of local authorities. Without their support and that of senior management CPD cannot be fully effective.

This Guide has been prepared with the main object of assisting organisations to carry out CPD — in their own interests, those of their employees and not least of clients and others working with them.

The Guide will also be of interest and value to those other partners in the CPD process, namely individuals and anyone concerned with the provision of CPD activities.

Philip Groves
Chairman
CPD in Construction Group

© 1991 The CPD in Construction Group

IBSN 0-9517304-0-1
Published by the CPD in Construction Group

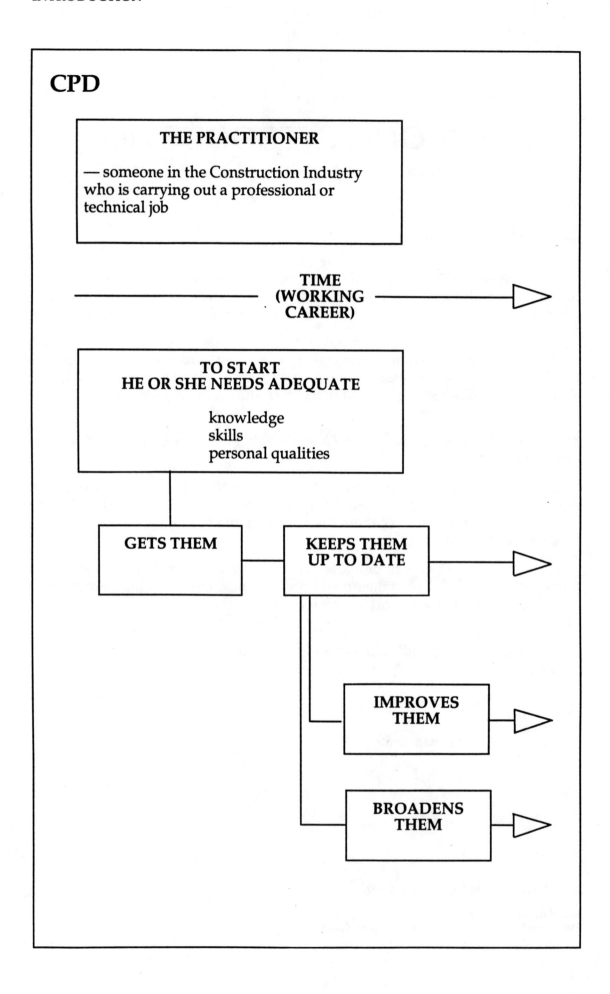

CPD

THE PRACTITIONER

— someone in the Construction Industry who is carrying out a professional or technical job

TIME
(WORKING
CAREER)

TO START
HE OR SHE NEEDS ADEQUATE

knowledge
skills
personal qualities

GETS THEM

KEEPS THEM
UP TO DATE

IMPROVES
THEM

BROADENS
THEM

2. CPD — A Definition:

CPD stands for Continuing Professional Development. There are, confusingly, other names for the same or similar such as continuing vocational training (CVT) and continuing education and training (CET). This shouldn't deter us. We'll stick with CPD.

The CPD in Construction Group defines Continuing Professional Development as...

> *"The systematic maintenance improvement and broadening of knowledge and skill and the development of personal qualities necessary for the execution of professional and technical duties throughout the practitioner's working life."*

which you will agree is pretty broad and far-ranging. It can extend from doing our own thing like reading the weekly trade journal or travelling to Timbuctoo (if they organise such things) for a week's conference on energy conservation. So it doesn't really lay down anything about how we should do it. This lets us get rid, right at the beginning, of any misconception that we might hold that CPD is about courses. It isn't. Courses are just one way. There are many others. Neither does the definition ask us to draw any lines of demarcation between education and training which saves us a lot of argument.

It allows us to get down to looking at the words more closely and reading between the lines.

Working backwards, the end of the definition tells us two things: that CPD is for the practitioner and it is for as long as he or she works.

But who is the practitioner?

Well we take for granted that he or she is in the construction industry and we read that he or she is carrying out a professional or technical job. In other words it's the job or the duties that count and not qualifications or membership of, for instance, a professional institution.

The meaning of the rest of the definition now falls more easily into place. It suggests that, for a practitioner to carry out his or her duties properly, adequate knowledge, skills and personal qualities are needed. It further suggests that the knowledge, skills and personal qualities must be continually topped up to keep them at an adequate level and subsequently improved and broadened so that they progressively get better.

None of these things should be a surprise to us so we can get on with how to achieve them.

"CPD is good for everyone; but not everyone wants it."

3.   CPD — For Whom?

FOR EVERYONE

Technicians, technologists, site managers, teachers, professionals, students, engineers, surveyors, designers (and why not typists, telephonists, receptionists?*).

Young graduates on industrial training, old know-it-alls moving/being moved sideways, upward movers marked for promotion, ambitious whizz-kids looking for designations.

Readers, listeners, watchers, lateral thinkers, tactile types, arguers, debaters. On-site, off-site.

Contractors, architects, quantity surveyors, planners, civil engineers, and landscape architects (and umpteen more, so please don't write and tell us that you've been forgotten).

BUT NOT FORGETTING

The Board, Senior Partners, Heads of Departments.

---

*   This is not a send up. CPD in its concept, if not in its strict definition,
      ought really to be for everyone. You owe it to them and your telephones
      will be answered more promptly; your letters might read better; your
      clients be impressed.

"Our in-house courses have had other indirect benefits: The individual who has researched the subject has learnt from the research and gained the status of an in-house expert; the staff have learnt from the research done by just one of their members; the lecturer/presenter has developed his/her own communication/presentation skills."

"QA/QM to BS 5750 (or ISO 9000) includes a requirement to review and meet training needs of quality related staff."

"Since we've taken over running our own CPD from an external consultant we've got a much better feel for the 'pulse' of our staff. Their reaction to CPD has markedly improved."

"In-house CPD develops presentational skills, is usually cost effective, improves communication within the company and maintains a monopoly of expertise."

"Whilst we will support a proportion of CPD post 1992 we do not intend to fulfil all the requirements. This will leave some of the quota to the individuals' initiative and discretion."

"Pressure of the 90s' will force management/trainers/organisers to maximise the use of their human resources."

"Professionalism is a state of mind. Anyone can be professional. An amateur can act professionally. A professional can act amateurishly."

4. CPD: The roles of the Organisation, the Professional Institution and the Individual

This word 'organisation' is what you want to make of it. It covers a multitude of working groups. It certainly includes companies, practices and the relevant departments of a local authority. Really it's anything that has people working for it. 'Professional institutions' and 'individuals' hardly need definition. But the roles and interaction of all three should be understood if only to appreciate how one complements the others.

There are misunderstandings. Some organisations take the view that CPD, as fostered by the institution, is unrelated to the real needs of *their* organisation. Others see the organisation's needs as differing from the individual's. Words like 'esoteric' and 'head in the clouds' are bandied about. There is probably some suspicion. This is unfortunate and counter-productive. Perhaps we could not do better than asking, 'What is the CPD role of the professional institutions and why to date do they seem to have monopolised it?'

Although it sounds a trifle pompous the institution does have a duty both to society and to its membership to see that members are properly qualified. This is done by ensuring that they pass examinations and undergo a limited amount of 'on-the-job' experience. The duty doesn't stop there however. It also extends to seeing that its members keep themselves up to date and develop. You expect it. The public expects it.

Of course the professional institution will be legislating only for its own members. After all they pay the 'subs'. It will not necessarily *provide* any CPD for its members; it might only lay down what is required of them leaving others to do the providing. By way of an incentive it might use the carrot or the stick.

What is done is not designed necessarily to have any influence on people outside the institution's ranks. But we would be foolish to ignore it. The members of the institutions are our people. The content and delivery of their CPD must interest us. If nothing else, learning of the institution's successes and failures should guide us and provide a source of material, ideas and events which we can use. At least one would expect that organisations could endorse the work of the professional institutions in encouraging excellence in their members. After all it presumably benefits the organisation which employs them. The total sum of its staff's excellence should be reflected in the organisation's own excellence and efficiency. We will come back to this. But now how about the individual's and organisation's role?

For those individuals wishing to take up or retain membership of a professional institution and later to advance in it there is considerable motivation. For many, membership is the key to their being able to practise their profession.

But those not in membership might view qualifications a little differently. After all the possession of personal qualities often ranks higher than qualifications in the esteem or pecking order of many organisations.

INTRODUCTION

However, as any marketing manager will tell you, those forming first impressions of an organisation do tend to judge it by the qualifications of the people in it. Later on in the relationship this changes and those working alongside an organisation begin to judge its efficiency on the abilities, broad-based experience and, particularly, personal qualities of its members whether qualified or unqualified.

The development of these skills should not be left to the professional institution. There is a vital role for the organisation in facilitating, providing, or at the least encouraging, its members of staff, qualified and unqualified, to carry out CPD and to improve their abilities and personal qualities.

But organisations do have other needs as well. The profile of any organisation differs from its competitors or peers in its aims, its structure, its procedures, its ethos. Each of these will/should be evolving and developing parallel to the organisation's markets, new technology and market-place; even to the changing aspirations of its employees.

The staff development implicit in the preparations needed for entry into Europe, for a quality assurance scheme or for the prospective framework for national vocational qualifications, to take just a few examples, is formidable. The development is as much of the team as of the individual. Because of this it cannot be provided remotely, at arms length, by the professional institution or some other external provider alone. It needs an in-house, organisation-based input written against an organisation background. The flavour might then be right.

Let's look at these needs in more detail.

"Succession planning is of growing significance and CPD towards this end is a key element to retention of staff."

"Technical updating by ploughing back in-house skills is now a priority."

"The organisation is now committed to taking over the further training needs of staff."

"Staff development is recognised as a management skill for all bosses not just the staff development manager."

SECTION TWO: DEFINING & ASSESSING NEEDS

5.   The Organisation's Needs

To keep ahead of the field an organisation needs continually to alter its shape. Radical changes such as a large increase in size to seize the advantage of new or perceived markets can be catastrophic if the organisation is not adequately prepared. Any diversification, such as a move out of depressed markets, whether voluntary or involuntary can bleed staff, capital and other resources, including energy, from the core operations of a previously successful organisation. There are remedies such as the purchase of already resourced organisations or the rapid recruitment of specialist staff. These have their drawbacks. The prudent investigation before the purchase of an organisation takes time particularly when its operations are unfamiliar. New staff rapidly recruited have to be too quickly thrown into the breach before their real as opposed to 'paper' quality is known.

In a perfect world capable, but redundant, staff in one department should be retrained to take up new responsibilities in another. The world isn't perfect but intelligent and sensitive anticipation allows management to ensure the broadening of staff's knowledge and skill so that the organisation always possesses a reservoir of suitable talent. This is good for staff morale and avoids the frustration when plum jobs are given to outsiders.

But the broadening of staff's skill and knowledge is not confined to readying them for changes in the organisation's operations. Because there must be some limit to the period spent in formal higher education students have tended to specialise in their chosen career and found little time to explore the worlds of those others in different fields who will later be working with them. Those with little formal higher education have picked up skills while at Nellie's knee following their chosen careers. Broadening, in both these cases however, has been a haphazard informal affair requiring pot-luck and ingenuity.

New skills can be roughly divided into two areas: soft skills, which are largely to do with personal development, and hard skills which have much to do with knowledge. Soft skills such as 'interviewing techniques', 'people management', 'funding presentations' or even 'answering the telephone' are used to develop the personal qualities of the individual giving more confidence and an ability to work with other people.

Hard skills have more to do with doing a job and keeping up to date with the changes that are going on around us; new technology, legal developments, and 'flavours of the month' such as coordinated project information, quality management and 1992.

There are no precise boundaries between hard and soft* skills and there certainly is no point in trying officiously to place them in one or other pigeon-hole. In many cases there will be a need for hard and soft skills to be tackled together. 'Communications' would be a barren subject if it did not take account of the pell-mell advances in information technology and its relevance and use. Often 'attitude' is the glue which sticks knowledge and skill together and is more important than either of them.

Client selection of those organisations which will be allowed to tender/design/manage/build a project has become more searching. The comparisons of price and contractual performance have now been supplemented by the addition of further hurdles which include assessments of past performance, team abilities, quality of personnel and so on. An organisation is likely to be judged as much on the qualifications, experience and personal qualities of its staff as its track record. These qualities include ability to market the organisation. They are essential skills. Professional qualifications are a bonus.

The learning of skills is not a task just for the individual on his or her own. It can be aimed at improving the efficiency of the team, the organisation, or the corporate whole. Learning does not imply being talked at or being taught. It can often be the finding of a better way to do something; a resolution come to by a group of people faced with a problem, who are able, by putting together or pooling their joint knowledge and skills, to provide answers, remedies and new procedures. But this begins to trespass on another area.

---

*   Some have reservations about this word 'soft' in case it gives others the impression that the skills are feeble or silly or easy. Those who have chaired difficult site meetings or stood in at 9.30 on a Monday morning for the telephone operator will not share these misapprehensions.

6.   The Individual's Needs

The individual is motivated in many and varied ways. Advancement in rank or stature is probably the greatest; bringing with it the recognition and the regard of his or her peers. The seal of rank or stature lies in job titles, car sizes and even possession of office coat stands, although cars, coat stands and other perks are as much rewards as symbols.

Worthwhile designations/qualifications are won more and more by educational achievements and parallel or subsequent work experience. Designations in the professional institution are maintained, higher designations achieved, through conformity with the rules of the institution. As we have seen, educational qualifications are only a part currency in obtaining institute designations. Nowadays an increasing number of institutions require evidence of CPD at the beginning of and thereafter progressively during their members' careers. The penalty for non-compliance is non-advancement or, at the worst, some form of de-frocking. The quantity, quality and range of CPD expected is usually well defined and its achievement recorded by credits, 'brownie points', in a variety of log books. A more detailed description of the arrangements and progress of individual institutions is described at Appendix 'B'.

The organisation distances itself from these arrangements at its peril. An obstructive, non-cooperative or even uninterested approach will frustrate the motivated staff member who increasingly expects his parent organisation to support, if not actually provide, opportunities for personal development and advancement of which CPD is a part. And, following logically, frustration can only in the long term dilute the quality, if not the number, of professionally qualified staff in the organisation.

It is wrong to believe that the individual's needs are somehow the antithesis of the organisation's needs. Clearly they can be different. Sometimes the individual will opt to acquire knowledge in an apparently remote subject that the organisation would not itself have chosen. Often the organisation will know before the individual of some skill needed as a result of fresh policy; for instance the hands-on experience required before the introduction of new or updated computer hardware or programmes.

Usually however the needs of the individual and organisation are complementary. We must assess the needs and coordinate them.

7. Assessing Needs

It becomes clear that to assess the *development needs* within our organisation we must look at individuals, the organisation and the world around us.

The individual, if honest and perceptive, will often be the best, but not definitive, guide to his own needs and shortcomings. Getting him to divulge these is not always easy.

The individual's peers and employers will often have strong but not necessarily objective views on his needs particularly where personalities are allowed to intrude. They will in any case have little idea of needs which have not yet shown themselves.

The organisation, with a policy of growth, development and diversification ought to be able to extend and expand this into a policy for future development of its staff. It should also be sufficiently sensitive and alive to current weaknesses that manifest themselves in staff or organisation and that need remedying.

Finally the organisation, particularly in the area of hard-skills, should be aware of developments, innovations and opportunities that are about to be 'flavours of the month' or, horrible thought, were on the bus that we've just missed.

The professional institutions' assessment of needs will be far less specific or prescriptive. Whilst some institutions have provided, authored or sponsored a considerable number of learning packages and courses these are best looked upon as a resource library rather than an obligatory menu of CPD provision.

The assessment of needs is most important. Without assessment CPD becomes a tail wagging the dog. Provision, without need, is a wasted resource.

But how do we do it?

"Assessment has influenced attitudes. Line managers now pay much more attention to the skills needed by their people."

"We assess our needs through a CPD committee drawn from all sections and levels of staff."

8.   Assessment Means

Before discussing elaborate systems of profiling, job descriptions and face to face interviews it might pay us to stand back and consider where we are and what we are about.

Some of us have not yet dipped our toes in. Some are up to our waists. The rest are swimming in one direction or another. None of us wish to be too ambitious for fear of getting out of our depth.

The means we adopt for assessment should be graduated to suit our degree of commitment or our size. The small organisation will easily be able to gather together the section heads, the department managers and, after tabling a menu of possible events, ask for priorities. To start with, these will usually be the acquisition of some hard skills, the need for which are glaringly obvious. The meeting will probably generate some discussion on content and audience and suggestions of other possible events to add to the list. This is 'ad-hocery' at its best. For many organisations it will suffice; providing as it does a co-operative and committed audience, a good cross section of needs and a low overhead. Top management must be involved to show commitment and to provide a corporate input.

If assessments are to be made through the medium of ad-hoc groups it is as well to provide a check that those not included, further down the line, are getting their own views expressed by whoever is deemed to represent them at the meeting. A suitable, indeed diplomatic, time to find out is at the beginning or end of an event under the guise of asking for comments and feed back.

Section heads/department managers/directors/ partners are invariably the best to determine CPD needs for the organisation. To assess needs for the individual they require some coaching in what they are looking for and how to do it. This is done by working with someone who will also provide continuity and objectivity throughout the organisation or department. The need for an organiser is discussed later.

Assessment of individuals' needs is best not done as an arm's length operation. People get suspicious and become 'not involved'. A simple question-naire setting out options with space for printing ratings and other ideas provides a good basis which can then be followed up by a face to face interview. This should be done regularly and used for learning from the past as well as planning the future.

Management might decide that there is a need for each member of a department or the organisation to attend a series of events — a core — as an obligation. These could be in the form of soft skills such as induction, safety or communication. They might be hard skills such as the introduction of a form of contract, a new drafting technique or 'green' materials.

The 'core' principles can be extended to a much more formal (and logical) system of producing a profile of skills and knowledge needed for a job and then comparing the individual's own profile against it.

There is clearly at this stage a danger that the system will take over and then smother the informality, the fun and the unconventionality. CPD should not be too overtly imposed. It can be gently introduced and voluntarily undergone by people who have a genuine desire and enthusiasm to fill their acknowledged gaps — their needs.

Someone must keep this enthusiasm bubbling.

SECTION THREE: SUPPORTING CPD

9. Management Ethos

On reflection this probably should have been dealt with at the beginning because it is the keystone of our CPD. Unless we get it right with the intent to succeed, rather than providing a cosmetic exercise to placate the organisation and delude the outside world, it were better not to have been done at all. It is easy to say 'I believe in/I value/I want' with all the drama and conviction of a consummate actor while at the same time withholding the resources, the moral support and the opportunity. This will make sure, if this is what we wanted, that it won't work. It is then easy to blame someone else for the failure and use it as an excuse for not trying it again.

How does one convince the Board or even the Board convince itself, that CPD is a worthwhile investment?

Someone has to have the temerity, the conviction, to demonstrate that things would/might have been different if something had been handled a little better. The Blogg's client interview might not have been such a debacle if the site manager had been qualified/the project manager had a clue about putting over the company's strengths/the company had a quality assurance scheme/the planner had heard of fast track.

Then someone has to ask how the site manager/the project manager/the planner/the company might be prepared a little better, how much the abortive estimate cost and in no time the Board should be resolving to do something. Then (maybe) someone will drop into the debate the words CPD.

This scenario can be rewritten. For the practice the touch-paper could be that client briefing, liquidation of the general contractor or those embarrassing service ducts through the columns. For the local authority planning department, how about starting with that last council presentation?

Now that management have decided that CPD, like an early morning jog, is 'good for you', it is a natural reaction for them to fire the starting pistol, turn over and go to sleep again. After all, their decision is indestructibly carved into the stone tablets of the Board minutes. They know that the next stage is the difficult one when reputations are more likely to be lost than won. Hopefully before the tablets make their journey down from the mountain someone will have added a postscript — whose responsibility it is and what authority that person is to be given.

"The staff development manager is over-committed especially with appraisals, schemes, CPD as well as running courses."

"I'd hoped to do this one myself but was overtaken by staff shortages and lack of time."

10. Organising

It is often said that to get nothing done you give it to someone who has plenty of time to do it. To get a lot done you blackmail, cajole, somehow persuade someone to do it for you who really has no time at all. This often works. It sometimes fails. Organising CPD properly is no sinecure but there are many ways of getting it done. These range from finding someone in the organisation who already has another job to employing someone specifically to do it. The choice depends on a number of factors; the size of the organisation; the breadth of CPD to be covered both initially and ultimately; the resources to be made available. It is not sensible to recruit on a temporary basis while you find out how it goes; it is unlikely to go at all until the appointee knows that success will provide a permanent perch. A knowledge of both training and education as well as the industry is not essential although it helps. Energy, enthusiasm, optimism, a potential to be liked and, above all, an ability to organise and motivate are essential to the job. CPD is not necessarily a discrete exercise. It can be part of the training function within an organisation always providing that the people performing the function do not have a fixation on craft and junior technician skills.

For the small practice or company the job of organiser will be very much part-time. It is unfortunate if the person appointed is chosen 'as the best of a bad job'/because he or she wasn't present at the meeting when the appointment was made/'because we haven't much for him or her to do over the next couple of months'. Selection of someone to organise is best based on authority and an enthusiasm for CPD. An evangelistic senior partner or director is often ideal; everyone then at least listens.

Whatever the size, large or small, of the organisation this business of authority is paramount. None can do the job efficiently if arrangements can be countermanded, people not made available or aims of presentations changed. The organiser is helped by being provided with a detailed job description that sets out his or her responsibility and authority. This should be circulated to everyone in the organisation. It will make clear the Board's/Senior Partners'/Managers' commitment and that they care!

It is a foolish organiser who does not involve and get the support of everyone from the Board/Senior partners/Managers down to those to be trained.

The Organiser must avoid being isolated, will need formal (and informal) continuing education and particularly in the role of assessor must seek and listen to the advice and ideas of staff and their managers. Whilst building up an armoury of outside facilities/resources/speakers/courses the organiser has an excellent opportunity to pick up advice, tips and ideas. The organiser must be a bit of a grape-vine, a listener, a scrounger, an optimist, a confidant(e).

A man (or woman) for all seasons...

"No more in-house courses because the budget has run out."

"Please tell me how much the others get."

11. Financing

Do men (or women) for all seasons come cheap? Does anything come cheap? But some things are cheaper than others and organisations must ask themselves what cost advantages there are in getting that estimate, avoiding that catastrophe, keeping those staff, recruiting those graduates, having some peace of mind. Only then can the budget be determined.

CPD can be free if you ignore the time, the floor space the beer and the sandwiches.

It can be expensive if it becomes an empire so have a budget; set out what you expect from it; don't make it an undefined part of the training budget; insist on costings and estimates and charge each cost-head in the organisation for their CPD services. You'll soon know whether it's being done properly or whether you can get it done better outside.

But you know all these things.

"Seminars are well attended but venue, subject and frequency must be planned to avoid overkill."

"CPD is good for both the organisation and the individual but we must structure it more than at present."

"Support from the rest of the organisation but not 'active' support to the organiser who tends consequently to shun anything more radical than 'interview techniques'."

"Small offices can be inefficient for in-house courses: too much trainer time per trainee day."

"The R & D group are active in presenting in-house courses and seminars."

"We prefer doing things in house without outside speakers. Everyone is on the spot and working within and for their own group."

"We needed a 'Planning Law Update'. Engaged one of the top planning lawyers. To pay the top line fee we got him to run two sessions in the day which was pretty exhausting but it enabled us to get a full house of 30 people from District Councils to each session. Their fees paid not only for the venue, the food and the speaker's fee but also allowed our own people to attend free. This helped the budget."

SECTION FOUR: PRESENTING CPD IN-HOUSE

12.   The Event — Aims & Audiences

An event is any method which an organiser adopts to put over to a specific audience a clearly defined subject. Events can take many forms; their shape, level and content depending much on the organiser's own ideas of the needs of the audience. Unfortunately the shape of an event can be distorted by a lack of resources; inadequate budgets, presenters, accommodation, time or even an inability on the part of the organiser to plan.

Before deciding on the form which an event should take it is essential that the organiser and his advisers define both the aim of the event and for whom it is intended. Not to do so is like chartering a boat without a rudder or crew.

The aim will seldom be described in a single title such as 'Quality Assurance' or 'Coordinated Project Information'. It has also to spell out the level of presentation, the areas within the title to be covered and the degree of audience comprehension to be aimed at, ranging from a general appreciation to a thorough working knowledge which the audience can take straight back to their work place and apply.

The aim should not be confused with the style or method of putting it over. This comes later.

While deciding on the aim the prospective beneficiaries, the audience, must be considered. The less diversified the audience the easier it becomes to define the aim especially in regard to levels. Specialists need a high level of content in their pet subject to prevent boredom. A very mixed audience with a varying depth of knowledge in the subject is often split between those who are 'turned off' because they know it all and those who quickly throw in the sponge because it is all above their heads.

When faced with this problem it is probably best to aim at a high enough level to satisfy the specialists. Even though frustrating for the others, it will at least make very obvious to them just how much they don't know. Certainly it is no answer to provide a level acceptable only to the lowest denominator while the rest are bored to tears.

While discussing mixed audiences two other aspects should be considered, joint events and common interests.

Assuming that resources are not unlimited, the organiser reaches a point where the potential size of audience is so small that it is uneconomic to run the event although there is clearly a need. It can be a mistake to dilute or contort the aim so that the event can suit a larger audience. This is the time to take a breath; count ten, and try to find an alternative way of providing it. It is not necessarily with an outside agency. Try other departments, other regions within the organisation and, if this fails, consider running an event jointly with some other organisation/s (see also chapter 16). Whilst they might learn something about you, inevitably you, the smarter cookies, will learn much more about them.

A last word on mixed audiences. Seldom do all have the same interests. But they usually have some common interests. With some ingenuity and careful planning it is possible to devise an event which gathers the mixed audience together for the common events, separates them for their specialist presentations and then brings them back together again to consider joint problems and solutions. The whole event can be spread over several sessions so that the administration and resources are not over loaded.

The duration of an event will depend very much on the magnitude of the 'aim'. It is tempting to keep each aim compact and short. Unfortunately the aims seldom conform to such treatment and it is counter-productive to trim viciously (or expand flatulently).

Attending a regular sequence of presentations can be habit-forming for the audience. It can also have a habit of tailing off if continued into eternity. One-off events dotted sporadically through the calendar need all the effort of a full-blown recruitment drive for each event.

Reference to the calendar and common sense will guard against unfortunate clashes with staff parties, school holidays and so on and save that profound embarrassment when the speaker having travelled 200 miles is faced by an audience of two: the organiser and an octogenarian bachelor.

"We try to ensure active participation by those attending but presenters are not always skilled..."

"Too much emphasis on formal courses and not enough on-the-job learning."

"The aim of the presentation was to allow the participants to understand an arbitration carried out in accordance with the terms of a building contract. The audience were regional members of the Institute. A friendly judge agreed to act the part of arbitrator and the late Ted Moult the aggrieved building owner. Several of the organisers spent a great deal of time concocting and distributing a background to the dispute.
"This worked excellently until the cross examination of the witnesses. The organiser had left too many gaps in their background paper. The witnesses' account of events became wilder and wilder as they enthusiastically extemporised. The lawyers made hay out of the conflicting evidence. Fortunately Ted Moult's humour saved the day.
"Marks: Enjoyed 10/10. Succeeded in aims probably 5/10.
"Moral: write a script or double the amount of research."

"By sending individuals on external seminars we have often been introduced to good speakers whose names are now filed for future reference."

"To help us with 'motivation' we asked a psychologist to make the presentation. It was very well received, different, but left us all worried about ourselves."

"Individuals need noticing. This involves talking with them rather than at them; discussing as opposed to instructing."

13. The Event — Style

Having decided on the aims and audience the organiser can consider the means that he or she will use to meet the first and satisfy the other.

But what does this audience expect?

Many older people — and sometimes even those who have only recently completed their full-time education — have an aversion to 'going back to school'. By this they mean sitting at formal rows of desks while a teacher talks at them.

There are other quite understandable hang-ups. Specialists in any field often have reservations when a non-specialist attempts to advise them. Those for whom there has been a long period since leaving formal education or training are hesitant to reveal their real or imagined shortcomings particularly to their younger colleagues. For those whose education was rudimentary this can be a major obstacle to making a relaxed contribution.

Those setting up an event must be aware of these fears and prejudices particularly when organising their first presentations. Later, when the participants have become more familiar with the style and pattern of events and less self-conscious in the process, it is possible for the organiser to become more venturesome, indeed to challenge and encourage the veterans to recount their experiences and suggest solutions.

Now to consider the means to be used in the preparation of our event.

There are countless alternatives, some simple, some elaborate, that are available to the organiser. If one discounts distance learning, the easiest is probably the in-house discussion group. For those dipping in their toes for the first time or with limited facilities or small audience numbers it can be fun and effective...but keep it simple.

An elaborate form of presentation is not necessarily the most effective. A subject, which is absorbing, relevant and timely coupled with a delivery which is punchy and concise, will have a greater impact on the audience than a presentation that is all glitter but no content. This applies however well-laced it might be with teaching aids and ploys to get an unresponsive audience standing on its seat throwing plastic cups at each other; an activity which goes under the name of 'audience participation'. More of this later.

Our event will usually aim to impart something new. We can do this in several ways. We might show a video and with the help of some course material let the audience do the rest; the presenter interrupting only to pull the audience back into line and end the session with a summary. We might ask a speaker to take over the whole event, which entails only introducing him and thanking him at the end. A combination of the two could have the speaker and video providing the core of the event and the presenter orchestrating the proceedings running the discussions drawing out the shy and controlling the exuberant.

To find a speaker who is knowledgeable about his subject and, more, able to communicate it, is not easy; the two do not always coincide.

Speaking publicly whether at a dinner table or lecturing is usually an acquired art; an art which sadly fewer seem to possess as they are supplanted by the highly remunerated and even higher regarded 'professional' performers. These are usually found in the ranks of retired or semi-retired professionals. They certainly provide entertainment but unfortunately because of the demands of the circuit, find it difficult to keep up to date with a rapidly changing industry. At the end of a comfortable session the audience will clearly have enjoyed themselves but later, on reflection, admit to disappointment when it is realised how the polished shell has contained a rather shrivelled, dry nut.

Although finding a good speaker is often a matter of trial and error and then trying to hang on to him there are, depending on the need, ways of growing one's own.

Probably every organisation and practice is staffed by people who have the required knowledge and who can update, or be up-dated on, that knowledge. All they often lack is the conviction and ability to put it over. With most this is a matter of gaining confidence and learning how to open their mouths, structure their presentation, and speak from adequate scripts with or without an overhead projector or prompt cards.

Some of these aspiring speakers are delicate flowers needing patience and encouragement. To start with they should be given short, easy tasks well within their capabilities. When later they have found confidence they will be able to pace themselves.

Home grown speakers have one distinct advantage over any others. They know the organisation; they know its foibles, its strengths and weaknesses. They find it easy to associate themselves with the audience. Unfortunately if they might have a defect it is that they lack experience of other companies and organisations and this can make them rather narrow-minded and parochial.

But even a single speaker presenting a well defined subject over one or more not over-long sessions does not guarantee success. Its advantages to the organiser are several. Easy to control. Only one person to brief and organise. No risks of overlap. But there are also disadvantages. Members of the audience are allowed to opt out/day dream/go to sleep and neither their comprehension or retention is tested. It is to avoid this that some form of audience participation could be introduced.

We have seen that the aim of a presentation might be to impart additional knowledge such as a technical advance. On the other hand it might be to build on the abilities already possessed by the audience and helping them to use them more effectively. But frequently the aim will be a mixture of both; imparting new knowledge and then deciding how that knowledge is best used and applied within the organisation.

This offers an ideal opportunity to let the audience fight back while at the same time making sure that they have taken in the message. It is the time for 'audience participation'.

There are a variety of ways of orchestrating this. The simplest form is a question/discussion period during or after the presentation. A good speaker will answer questions and then use his own questions as the basis for debate and argument. This humility (even if feigned) on the part of a speaker, who shows he can listen, will often disarm an audience and turn it from suspicion into active cooperation.

More sophisticated forms of audience participation are case studies, role-playing, projects and hands-on experience.

Case-studies have many forms. Essentially they set the subject of the presentation into either a real or an imagined framework. Participants can associate themselves with the situations in which they are placed and organisers can introduce machiavellian trips and traps into the scenario. Many case-studies are over-devised demanding the assimilation of much superfluous information — even to the sometimes esoteric lives of the characters so that the proceedings deteriorate into something resembling a soap-opera. Some case-studies are so simplified that they do not mirror accurately a real-life situation which is seldom clear-cut, black and white.

Role playing which is a form of case study requires participants to adopt roles or characters. These can be ones with which they are familiar or completely new to them; the choice depending very much on what outcome is required. The unfamiliar role is ideal when, for instance the aim is to promote a team ethos where the other person's problems and point of view have to be understood. But to be properly done it requires the creation of a background so that the role-player is fully aware of all the constraints, procedures and aims of the person whom he or she is playing.

It is difficult to put over in the abstract, technical subjects normally requiring the back-up of equipment or hardware. Programming, the use of computers, concrete testing is put over far more efficiently (and sticks) if the audience is allowed hands-on experience. The construction of intricate components is better soaked up in the manufacturer's works or on site. These are all potentially exciting and memorable.

There are a variety of styles and combinations of styles for your event. The style should be chosen to help presentation, to enliven, to instruct, to highlight the aim. Each style requires a different performance and preparation. An event is rather like a film or play. For style read stage directions...for organiser read the producer, director...

... (and scene shifter)!

"Residential courses for staff at all levels with a social context: this is of special benefit."

"When asked what was most memorable about the lunch-time meetings he answered, 'The lunches.' "

14. Locations, Times, Accommodation

Location of the organisation's bases, catchment areas, offices will often dictate the venues of events; the logistics of minimum travelling for the largest number are a powerful argument for in-house meaning literally within the office. Beer and sandwiches squeezed among meticulous taking-off sheets or CAD keyboards and monitors can be incongruous and particularly off-putting if the office chosen is the lair of your most un-favourite person. (Because its his chair he will preside at his desk as if the whole event is his also.) Lucky is the organisation with a purpose-made meeting room with comfortable chairs and refreshments on tap. The Board/Senior Partners' room meets the specification but is seldom offered.

There is much to be said for getting away altogether from the office/site. The phone can't ring (if you ban mobile sets) and somehow everyone is so much more relaxed and concentrating on their part in the event rather than their day-to-day routine. It's also good for us to realise how easily people get on without us; delegation, after all, is one of our soft skills!

Back rooms of pubs are excellent but you must restrict the liquid input and remain firm. (Memo; put the cost of refreshments in the budget.)

If the style of the event needs equipment think delivery, security, insurance, power sources, and if it's someone else's — that it works, is compatible and is realistically priced.

Timing is always difficult. An evening event disposes of an evening and is hard on commuters who have an invidious choice of filling in the time between the office and the event or going home and then returning. They often don't.

Week-end events are a wow for the organiser but difficult for sportsmen, family men, gardeners, anyone other than devotees (but families can be bribed).

Day events which underline our dedication to real CPD, letting us get down to the subject properly and in depth, also keep people out of offices, off telephones, off sites. Emergencies will always win and who will argue when a job/a contract/a client is at stake although it grows a bit thin when a department always manages a full day of emergencies involving all its staff.

A favourite is probably lunch-time or what is now called 'twilight' i.e. three quarters of an hour before knocking off time to three quarters after. Both organisation and individual contribute equally. For those in the far-flung empire such as site managers this is not so easy and they must leave their jobs much earlier in the afternoon. This might be inconvenient and can be disastrous when the site manager has no assistant who will take over; 4.30 being the time when the tower crane breaks down/ready-mix dries up/bricky gang packs up/architect makes a site visit (I say, where's the person in charge?).

Take heart; resource planning is another desirable skill.

"Videos are 'good servants, bad masters'."

"A bigger choice of videos would be useful (they provide back-up if the speaker does not arrive)!"

15. Aids To Presentation

This could have been covered under style. It wasn't so we'll deal with it now.

There have been a number of visual aids over the years which have helped presentations, helped presenters and ultimately helped the audience. The earliest was the black-board.

These aids undoubtedly helped us to retain information because two senses were employed; hearing and seeing. If your talk was incomprehensible your audience might at least pick up something from the screen.

After the blackboard came the flip-chart which obviated the need for writing during the presentation. When you got to the end of one sheet you just flipped it over. If your handwriting was bad you could get someone else to write it for you.

The overhead projector much used even today allows a rapid change of foils which can depict pictures, book extracts, diagrams and ones own notes. Presenters familiar with them use the notes as cribs. Those unfamiliar with them get the foils out of order and end in chaos.

Slides have been best displayed through a carousel and projector. It is vital that sufficient time is spent before an event to ensure that the slides are in focus, in the proper order and the right way round. It is disconcerting for buildings to grow downwards through the foggy dew!

Two or more projectors, coordinated together, can transform a session of 'looking at my slides' into a professional presentation particularly if there are good synchronised indirect controls. (The presenter shouting 'all-change' to his assistant does give the impression of journey's end at Euston.)

The visual aids described have had a commendable effect on presentations which have subsequently been better thought out and structured. They have not only kept the audience awake but provided them with check-lists for the obligatory notes which will be kept for a year or two and then thrown out with the old diaries.

A few of us will remember when visual became audio-visual with the introduction of records and, later, tapes thus dispensing with the live speaker. These were excellent for solo-distance-learning and arctic expeditions but not so good for larger audiences who find the anonymity similar to that experienced in the emergency back-up marquee when the church is overflowing at the wedding. Who did she finally marry?

Audio-visual in the shape of videos is now with us. Chosen wisely and used as case studies a background or appetite-wetter they will enhance most events. Some will provide an indoor audience with an outdoor perspective. Others will provoke and challenge the audience so that it bubbles over with contention and debate. Some will dispense with the guest speaker.

Learning packs that often go with the videos will save the organiser or presenter much time in preparation. Beware of circulating these papers before the night. In theory it's fine to have a knowledgeable audience but too many leave the reading for the train journey in and then find 'page three' in their tabloid is more attractive.

Beware also of out-dated/black and white/generic videos unless the event is billed as 'historical'. Know that because of the high quality of television in the UK audiences are put off by videos that come below that bench-mark. Whatever you do don't hire a video for arrival on the day before your event. It either won't arrive or worse will turn out to be completely inappropriate for your purpose. Get a preview. Pick it up yourself. Buy one.

Interactive videos, mainly on generic subjects, are becoming slowly more available. The hardware requires quite heavy investment as does the production. This will probably become less of a problem as techniques and technology improve.

All 'Aids to Presentation' are not always pieces of equipment. Case studies and teaching packages, mentioned earlier, are available from a number of sources. They make the planning much easier and the event more exciting. Mundane though they might seem samples, models, product literature and films and trade association exhibitions can provide economical contributions to an event (but watch for the too-enthusiastic hype).

Keeping aware of presentation aids available is a time-consuming job. Appendix C suggests some sources of information. Get on the right mailing lists. (Memo: allow in the budget for building up a library of material that you will use again not forgetting the hardware you will display it on.)

You have now determined the ingredients; the What, Where and How.

It is time to put them into the pot and stir...

16.   Putting It Together

It is now that everything should start to come together. We have support and a policy; we have assessed our needs and this has enabled us to determine our aims, audience and our first event. The organiser now has the job of organising, coordinating and communicating.

Expertise is an ingredient necessary for most events. It might lie within the organiser's capability. It might be talent hidden away in some part of the organisation albeit another department or another region; often it will come in the form of some outside agency; a self-professed expert. The organiser must — and here diplomacy is needed — ensure that the candidate can project himself, is knowledgeable and will accept a brief and stick to it. The brief must cover content, level and timing to avoid over-runs, over-laps with others' presentations and irrelevance. Full notes to be provided weeks before the event for circulation to the others participating are always promised. They usually arrive, in an incomprehensible long-hand, on the day of the event and frequently with a request for some rare piece of projecting equipment available only from the continent.

After a time the organiser will have worked out some formalities, a check list, some rules to make sure that presenters have the right equipment and do not arrive half way through the event because the train broke down/it wasn't clear where the meeting was to take place/'I thought you said start at 11pm!'

The coordinator will also have another check list to ensure that the meeting place is booked, the right number of chairs and tables will be set out, and that there is an adequate amount of refreshments during a natural break.

Lastly, the question of paper-work. There is nothing more disconcerting than an audience, provided with the unabridged text of the presentation, sitting heads down like reporters at a local parliamentary candidate's press conference, checking the delivery word for word and turning over the pages as if on command. Unless the acoustics are particularly bad or the audience stone deaf confine the issue of paper work before the meeting to stuff that is strategically vital or can only be read with difficulty on the projector. Issue the rest after the event is over. To be even sharper bind it all in a cover bearing your own livery.

You have now started building up a reference manual...

"Recruits to the company are increasingly interested in the development element of their terms and conditions of service."

"The carrot is the provision of a learning opportunity."

"Demographic changes are approaching and if training is given a high profile it may well influence the decision of young people to join us."

17. Incentives

For most individuals personal improvement is self-motivated. The motivation is strengthened if there is some reward. The reward might be recognition by the employer, exemplified by promotion or a quick slap on the back. It might be recognition by the professional institution resulting in higher designation (or just being allowed to stay in!!). Time spent on personal improvement however can demand sacrifices and sometimes these threaten the domestic structure. In the last twenty years there has been a marked decrease in the numbers attending local professional institution evening events. Presumably this has resulted from a greater expectation of the standards of such events, competition from other activities such as television or, most likely, pressure from the family. It could of course, dreadful thought, be evidence of less self-motivation. This makes it even more important that rewards are available and used.

Graduates entering companies, possibly taking advantage of their scarcity, have turned their interviews into inquisitions in which they have sought information about the training policy of the company or practice. While this is a welcome change from enquiries about the colour of the 'perk' car it also indicates that personal improvement is taking a more German/Japanese look.

Particularly in times of recession, where every expenditure is carefully weighed and staff reduced to a minimum, companies and practices are more concerned with short-term survival than the longer term advantage derived from training. It is an invidious choice for departmental managers who have to balance day-release for their motivated staff against the extra burden thrown on the hard pressed remaining staff with all the resentment that this can cause.

Most companies and practices find that compromise and even-handedness works. By staging events that straddle 'on' and 'off' times, at lunchtime or in the early evening, the individual and the organisation each donate something. Some organisations demand attendance as part of their working rules; others genuinely consider attendance as voluntary — with no recriminations for absentees. (This doesn't mean they're not noticed however.) Payment, other than expenses, for training out of company or practice time is rare. Fees for outside courses are usually paid by the organisation or, at worst, divided between organisation and trainee.

Unfortunately expenses do not at the moment qualify for VAT relief for the individual although this is a battle still being fought. However for the firm the cost of CPD is treated as training expenses out of untaxed income.

"Life is full of successes and failures. We have our share of both."

"Even though we gauge success and plan new events on the basis of attendances and favourable response afterwards one or two disasters have still occurred."

"We try to ensure that an opportunity to implement learning will occur very soon afterwards."

"One should prepare for disappointment — the delegates for whom you have striven long and hard to prepare an interesting event will moan that it is taking them away from important work; starts too early, finishes too late; the food was too much, too little, too hot or too cold; the speakers were too loud, too quiet, or too boring and the topic(s) not covered in enough detail, too detailed, or simply irrelevant.
"In short it's a great life if you don't weaken!"

18.   Audit

A piece of jargon to remind us that there is more to all of this than a highly applauded event. Our aim was to provide for the needs of our staff. Did it work?

We need to know for two main reasons. Has each member of the staff gained as much as we intended from the experience? Has he or she made the difficult transition from theory into practice? Can we put a tick in those particular boxes or does he or she need more?

Did those attending rate the content, style, level of presentation as indifferent, bad or awful? If they did we must learn lessons rapidly and boldly because we are about to lose a reputation fickle though it might have already been.

Ways to find out about the individual's gain range from a direct rating, which could include tests and an objective feed-back from heads of departments and sections, to a more relaxed person-to-person relationship between organiser, manager and individual. You take your choice.

It is important to decide what you are auditing. Attendance at an event or obtaining a skill? Present day 'brownie points' given by institutions seem to focus more on attendance — presumably done on the premise that some skill must rub off in the process. If you are rating skills then this has to be gauged through performance on the job or some form of test carried out at the end of, or preferably sometime after, the event.

Feed-back on the event can be hurtful. The organiser must brace him or herself for destructive criticism whilst welcoming that which is constructive. Attenders will not, and should not be expected to, make allowance for badly-disciplined presenters, accidents or missing the target. Precious commodities, their time and opportunity, are being wasted. Fulsome praise should be examined with some cynicism. You're not that good!

However, be happy that people want to discuss themselves and their CPD with you.

"Commercial providers tend to be more expensive than the education sector but are often more responsive to real life and less theoretical."

"...has been most successful. A top class presentation at £1,000 for 40 odd people against £250 per person for the same in London AND no travelling."

"Local professional institution courses not used enough — they have a vital role."

"Consultants must be well briefed and prepared to deliver what the client wants."

"In-house CPD might not be accredited. It should be."

SECTION FIVE: OUTSIDE AND CONCLUSION

19. Integration with Other Provisions

Enough has probably been written already about the mechanics of CPD provisions in the professional institutions. Theirs will be a continuing evolution and their use of the stick as incentive will surely supplant the carrot more in those institutions where there is a restricted entry than in those where anyone can practice. With this change in emphasis it is likely that events will increasingly be moderated and accredited and improve in quality. More will be provided at Regional and Centre levels. Organisations would be foolish not to avail themselves of opportunities to work with any institutional provider.

Post-graduate education, particularly, MSc's and diplomas, are being provided by polytechnics, colleges and universities on a larger scale. Many are on a modular basis covering a fairly wide range of subjects. Some, for instance, provide opportunities for staff wishing to ready themselves for Europe by presenting modules on foreign languages and an understanding of commercial practice on the continent. The post-graduate courses can be used in whole or in part.

Other courses can be arranged away from the traditional course structure and out of institutional hours which allows organisations to tap particular academic skills and current research.

Special courses in educational institutions can also offer specialist equipment such as mass computer hardware. This facilitates hands-on experience and eliminates the queue before the participant has his or her go at the keyboard. The group use of computers also enables the organiser to consider the use of computer-based management games many of which are being used regularly in institutes of higher education.

Firms of management consultants have a thriving business presenting CPD courses, often under another name, to the industry. They clearly present many opportunities for the hard-pressed organiser and obviate the need for most of the hassle connected with an event. Just fill in the application form, attach the cheque and someone, somewhere should satisfy a need; an ideal way of providing for the small minority. Unusually attractive meeting-places, good food and wine and a welcome opportunity to swop opinions and ask questions with one's peers. Often the presenters are good, the style is slick and events benefit from having been done before. Two difficulties might present themselves. The price is not always cheap (although nothing like putting on an event for just one or two people) and quality/relevance/depth is an unknown quantity. Many people race back from these events full of new ideas and enthusiasm. Unfortunately others crawl back frustrated because the event didn't come up to the billing.

It is impossible for the organiser to visit every event. He or she can use staff for reconnaissance and require them to provide a report on their return. A reasonably objective list of suitable course providers can then be drawn up and used in the future.

Consultants invited to organise or take part in the in-house event are more likely to satisfy the organisation's need and either will prepare their own suggested brief or be happy to follow someone else's . They will usually bring their own learning materials and teaching aids and provide speakers/presenters.

The use of outside resources — institute, education, consultant — can be a very useful weapon in the organiser's armoury. It is certainly not an admission of failure and, often, is an economical, sensible, alternative way of cracking a nut.

20. A Tailpiece

The views expressed in this Guide are those of the author helped by a number of organisations in our industry who, to use our by now well-worn metaphor, are swimming strongly enough in one direction or the other, to be able to find time to talk of their experiences and offer advice. The advice is not all unanimous. Organisations vary for instance on the help which they should give to their staff in meeting the CPD requirements of professional institutions. We think that these differences do not arise from parsimony but often from a healthy belief that there is a time for paternalism to stop and the individual to follow his own bent.

There is quite naturally considerable difference in the ethos of each organisation rather as there is a difference in its management style, its aims and its market.

But most striking is the unanimity expressed by all organisations in their belief in the need for CPD and the importance of themselves performing a large part in its planning, provision and support. In other words to invite it 'in-house'.

There is further unanimity in the worrying scenario to be drawn of an industry, an organisation or an individual without CPD. Rapid technological advance, greater markets with implied greater competition, the demands of employees, an acceptance of the paucity of present provisions all are powerful arguments for doing something quickly and then keeping it going.

The Guide has tried not to be prescriptive in its solutions but rather to paint with a wide palette allowing the reader to select the tones and hues which seem most appropriate against the background of his or her own organisation.

If there are underlying messages to be drawn from the Guide they are probably that:

- Without the authority and evangelism of the person or people at the top of the organisation, CPD will wilt and die.

- CPD is only a name for some things which most of us have been doing sporadically and badly for most of our lives.

- CPD is a joint effort between the organisation, the individual, the institution and the event provider. All must contribute before taking from it.

It is clear that the good organiser in his or her personal commitment and enthusiasm can lift attendance at the event from being a dutiful chore to fun, excitement and opportunity.

We would thank all who have contributed and criticised. They are listed elsewhere. We hope none of the comments or quotations are attributable or, if they are, that the Board is still abed.

LIST OF APPENDICES

A   Some Notes On Compilation Of The Guide

B   CPD In The Professional Institutions

C   Sources Of Information

D   A Choice Of Events

E   Acknowledgements

F   CPD In Construction Group

APPENDICES

Some Notes on the Compilation of the Guide

The Guide, commissioned by the CPD in Construction Group, is based on and was preceded by a survey of organisations which were known to be running their own CPD. The survey was not aimed at providing statistics but rather to elicit advice and examples of good and bad practice.

The Guide has been written by John Walkerdine, MBE Director of CERCI Communications. His knowledge of construction education and training stems from a lifetime in the industry where he has held positions ranging from chief surveyor in an architectural practice to managing director of his own building company. He has also served on the CNAA, NCVQ and B/TEC councils and is still involved with education in his own institute where he chairs the Committee for Recognition of External Awards.

CERCI Communications is sponsored by the Building Centre Trust. Amongst many other areas of its work it makes video packages for the construction industry including the CPD in Construction Group's 'Better Building' Series.

The draft Guide has been circulated for comment to the various respondents whose names appear in the acknowledgements at appendix E. Many of these took part in both the survey and subsequent interviews.

To give an idea of its style and purpose an extract from the survey questionnaire is given at the end of this section. For those who would like to use it as a check list for their own organisation the full questionnaire is available from CERCI Communications.

Extracts from the Questionnaire

SURVEY FOR CPD IN CONSTRUCTION GROUP

Introduction

This survey is being conducted to find out about those companies, practices and organisations who are running their own in-house Continuing Professional Development.

It is hoped that Industry as a whole might learn from their experiences.

The exercise is not a statistical one nor will the report on the survey divulge any names or identifiable details of those who have helped us.

Some of the questions asked cannot be answered with a simple "yes" or "no" and, although we have at times provided a list of possible answers, these are far from exhaustive. We have therefore left plenty of space for you to add ideas and alternatives of your own, to comment on the questions or even to add anecdotes if these will help you explain yourself better to those who will later learn from YOUR experiences. Please do not be put off by the sheets of paper. Answer as much as you have time for or think is relevant. We will be grateful for that.

Form of the Questionnaire

The questions are divided between several sections. Please read them through before starting to write answers.

The first section covers "planning for CPD in-house". It is intended to find out how, for your organisation's purposes, you define CPD and what you expect the individual and your organisation to get out of it.

The CPD in Construction Group defines CPD as:-

'The systematic maintenance, improvement and broadening of knowledge and skill and the development of personal qualities necessary for the execution of professional and technical duties throughout the practitioner's working life.'

You will probably find little fault with the definition but

Q.1   Do you confine your organisation's provision of CPD to any particular level or section of staff?

               (tick one)   YES   NO

       and if so what? ....

Q.2   Do you consider that certain parts of education or training are not strictly your organisation's concern and should be left to the individual or others (eg. Professional Institution)?

       (Tick those on the list which are not your affair)

               Continuing education such as a Masters degree; PT release leading to qualification.

               CPD quota required by an individual's institution.

Q.3   What are your objectives for the individual?

       (Tick those applicable)

       To prepare him for:

               other jobs in the organisation

               promotion

               general broadening of skills

       To enable him to:

               get qualifications

               keep up with high-tech (hard skills)

               work with others

               learn skills of managing (soft skills)

       To meet his pressure to be given more education and training as of right.

       Others ....

The next section is about the way in which you decide your priorities and choice of subjects.

Q.4   Which of the following most nearly represent your method of deciding on the needs which your CPD must meet.

(please tick those appropriate).

An assessment by individuals of their perceived needs

An assessment by the organisation of the individuals' needs

An assessment by the organisation of its needs

An ad-hoc decision based on the "flavour of the month", resources available or what is pretty sure to get a good audience

A bit of all these

Q.5   How do you assess your needs?

(please tick those appropriate)

Regular analysis of staff needs

Individual interviews

Discussions with groups of staff or heads of departments

Job evaluations

Periodic reviews resulting in long-term programmes

Others ....

The next section covers the resources and organisation which have to be found and coordinated for in-house training

Q.6   Do you have a person in the organisation who has special responsibility for CPD?

(please tick)   YES   NO

(How was he selected; how much time does he have; how much authority)

Q.7   Is the budget

        specifically for CPD?

        part of the training budget?

        something to be fought for?

        How much per head

Q.8   Are employees allowed

        full time off during working hours to attend CPD courses?

        time off on a half organisation/half employee basis?

        no time off?

        (Do you pay them for any mode of attendance?)

Q.9   Is attendance at CPD courses

        compulsory?

        voluntary?

        a mixture of both?

        (what carrots are there?)

Q.10   What sort of resources are put at your disposal?

        accommodation

        viewing equipment

        refreshments

        other ....

Q.11   Are you training the trainers? (How?)

                            YES   NO

(Editors Note: The complete questionnaire ran to 23 questions)

APPENDICES

CPD in the Professional Institutions

As part of their learned society role it has been traditional for the professional institutions to offer a range of activities and services designed to assist their members to improve their knowledge and skill. These have included - lecture meetings, seminars, workshops, information services, technical reports, periodicals and other publications.

Many of these services have been provided free as part of the membership subscription while others have been provided for a separate subscription or other payment. In the past, the take up of these services has however been minimal in many cases.

Members of professional institutions have an obligation to observe rules of professional conduct and competence and a formal system of continuing professional development (CPD) is considered necessary to support this requirement.

Considerable progress has been made in recent years in the development of CPD in the professional institutions which have concentrated on motivating their members and further developing of means of assisting them in carrying out the required CPD. The following indicates the present position:

Chartered Institute of Building (a)

Under Rule 5 of its Rules of Professional Conduct, a member is required to keep himself informed of new thought and development in building. Following an initial period when CPD was voluntary it was made obligatory for new members from 1989 and from 1990 for all other members.

The Institute has published a CPD Record Card and guidelines recommending members to undertake a minimum of 20 hours per year made up of 'Direct CPD' — those activities which contribute to improved professional performance — and 'Indirect CPD' — those activities which contribute to personal development.

Certain events at local Centres of the Institute (a total of 52 in the UK) can be 'designated' as CPD events and the Centre Chairman authorised to issue Certificates of Attendance to those attending them. A CPD Handbook has been produced for Centre chairmen.

Building companies and training organisations offering short courses and seminars can have them accredited and be authorised to issue attendance certificates.

Notes   (a) Member of the CPD in Construction Group
          (b) Associate Member of the CPD in Construction Group

A network of recognised CPD Study Centres has been established throughout the UK and in certain overseas countries and Regional Councils have appointed CPD officers to co-ordinate CPD activities in each Region.

Applicants for the Professional Interview or for Fellowship are required to indicate the CPD they have undertaken and discuss it in interview.

Chartered Institution of Building Services Engineers (a)

CIBSE is committed to CPD in the firm belief that both the engineer as an individual and the profession as a whole will benefit from participation.

The first objective of the Institution's Five Year Plan for 1987 to 1991 was defined as the need "to develop and instal an effective policy for Continuing Professional Development for members" and a CPD Committee was set up to implement it.

An Institution policy and a Record of CPD Activities for completion by members have been published.

CIBSE is a full nominating and authorised body of the Engineering Council. As a learned society and qualifying body it provides a range of technical meetings, conferences and seminars organised either directly by headquarters, through its 13 regions or in partnership with other professional institutions, trade associations and government departments. Its main thrust in technical information is through the publication of guides, technical memoranda, reports etc. Its monthly trade journal 'Building Services' is supported by two technical journals published quarterly.

A brochure giving details of courses provided by academic establishments and other bodies and a programme of seminars provided by the Institution have been published. Notes for the guidance of course providers are being prepared.

Evidence of CPD activity is required when application is made for higher classes of membership.

Institution of Civil Engineers (a)

The Institution requires civil engineers following graduation to undertake a minimum of 30 days 'off-the-job' training before they can achieve chartered status.

After full Corporate Membership has been obtained the Institution recommends that members keep themselves up to date by Continuing Education and Training (CET).

A formal scheme of Continuing Professional Development approved by the Council of the Institution is based on the following principles:

The Institution should whole-heartily support CPD based on a voluntary system.

A self-monitoring procedure should be implemented, based on a personal record book which is being produced.

The Institution should act as a focus for providing courses and should issue guidelines for the selection of suitable courses. The Institution should not formally approve these courses.

A total average of five days CPD each year should be undertaken.

Institution of Structural Engineers (a)

In November 1985 the Institution established a voluntary CPD scheme to come into full operation in 1988. Each Branch Committee has a member responsible for CPD and the Institution has a full time CPD officer at Headquarters.

Members are required to keep a record of CPD activities and provide a written self-assessment at appropriate intervals. Such records are assessed at each change of class of membership and at intervals for members continuing in the same class of membership.

A CPD Diary has been published to enable members to state their intended short and long term CPD objectives, means of achieving them and a record of the activities undertaken.

The Institution runs programmes of short courses at the Headquarters and in the Branches.

A handbook to assist in the implementation of the CPD scheme by members, Branches of the Institution and firms is being published.

Royal Institute of British Architects (a)

In July 1987 the RIBA Council decided that from 1992, a personal commitment to CPD would be a requirement of membership.

A rolling programme of funding has been made available to the RIBA's Regions to establish a nationwide CPD service and CPD managers are in post in the majority of Regions. A wide range of services is provided to assist members with their CPD eg. -seminars, courses, lectures and other events, the publication of CPD Newsletters, counselling and the provision of open learning material on sale or hire.

A number of a series of 300 open learning packages have been produced. They cover total project management; architectural practice management; building contract procedures, claims and arbitration; building law, strategy requirements and legal responsibilities.

The following proposals have been adopted for implementation by 1992:

that 35 hours of CPD (equivalent to five days) should be the essential minimum per annum with a further 35 hours being desirable in addition.

that each member should be expected to prepare a Personal Development Plan (PDP) and that all work which has been identified in a PDP should 'count' as being essential, provided that the Plan has been discussed with another member and recorded.

preparation of a database on CPD facilities that are available.

Royal Institution of Chartered Surveyors (a)

The RICS CPD Scheme laid down in Institution Bye-laws and currently applying only to Professional Associates elected on or after 1 January 1981 and to members transferring to Fellowship will be extended to all members from 1 January 1991.

The Scheme requires members to undertake and record a minimum of 60 hours of CPD in each three year period until retirement.

Members applying for transfer to Fellowship will continue to have to demonstrate their observance of the Bye-law in the three years prior to their transfer application.

The Scheme is monitored annually on a sample survey basis — members being required to submit their CPD records.

An Owlion audio cassette 'CPD and all that' has been produced to explain the reasons for the introduction of CPD, the various ways in which it can be undertaken, its benefits, the assistance that is available from the RICS and comparison with the CPD activities of other institutions.

The Institution publishes a CPD Guide, Record Card, Divisional Guides and a CPD Newsletter.

Royal Town Planning Institute (a)

The Institute requires members to maintain their professional competence under Clause 4 of the Code of Professional Conduct. How this is done is the responsibility of the individual member, but the Institute advises a minimum of 50 hours CPD over two years. Guidance to members has been produced along with a record card and members are recommended to assess their CPD requirements and develop a Personal CPD Plan. Guidance has also been produced for local authority managers and employers and it is intended to produce similar guidance for employers and managers in the private sector.

The Institute is currently reviewing options for a future strategy. It has commissioned a number of Distance Learning Packages, and is publishing a combined guidance and record sheet.

Architects and Surveyors Institute (b)

From January 1991, members will be obliged to undertake a minimum of 20 hours CPD per year.

Detailed proposals are being finalised and discussed with the Area Officers who will have a major role to play in the registration and recording of CPD.

British Institute of Architectural Technicians (b)

This Institute's CPD Scheme has been in operation since 1985 and is co-ordinated on a national basis by the Institute's Marketing Department and National Technical Committee.

The Scheme requires members to complete a minimum of 120 units of CPD each year which can comprise any combination of differently weighted activities in four categories. These range from CPD in the simplest passive form (reading/listening/watching) to active study through short courses, specialised research and distance learning. A special weighting is given to events organised by BIAT.

On completion of the Scheme the member is awarded a Certificate of Compliance. The Scheme is co-ordinated at Regional level by a network of 16 Technical Development Co-ordinators.

The Institute sponsors the Design Technology Project, a distance learning course of 101 three-hour modules, based at Sheffield City Polytechnic, and has arranged a Continuing Education Diploma for architectural technicians via B/TEC.

Incorporated Association of Architects and Surveyors (b)

A formal scheme requiring all members to undertake CPD is being introduced. CPD Record Book and advice on carrying out CPD will be made available.

Members are regularly reminded of their obligations under the IAAS Codes of Professional Conduct, to strive to maintain and improve their professional knowledge and contribute to the best of their ability to the knowledge and understanding of their profession as a whole.

Institute of Maintenance and Building Management (b)

A formal scheme of CPD is being implemented with encouragement to maintain a record of the training undertaken and submission of the record as part of a professional interview to establish the member's professional standard.

Institution of Civil Engineering Surveyors (b)

A CPD scheme applying to all corporate members will be implemented by 1992. A weighted points scheme for various types of activity with an average annual figure of 25 hours is proposed.

Institute of Clerks of Works

A Council member has been appointed Chairman of CPD with the initial task of studying the CPD needs of clerks of works. A standing committee for CPD will be established shortly.

The Landscape Institute

The Institute has embarked on the setting up of a formal CPD programme.

APPENDICES

Sources of Information

British National Film & Video Catalogue

> The British Film Institute,
> 21, Stephen Street,
> London W1.
> Telephone:071 636 3289

British Universities Film & Video Council

BUFVC provides an information service for those seeking AV materials on higher education subjects. It produces newsletters and catalogues.

> British Universities Film & Video Council,
> 55, Greek Street,
> London W1V 5LR.
> Telephone:071 255 1444

'Commissioning a Programme'

A guide to the commissioning, production and use of audio-visual programmes. 63 pp A5 price £10.00.

> Published by International Visual communications Association,
> Bolsover House,
> 5, Clipstone Street,
> London W1P 7EB.
> Telephone:071 580 0962

'Construction Preview' Catalogue of Audio-Visual Material

Catalogue of all audio-visual material produced for educational purposes for the construction industry. Twice yearly newsletter to keep the catalogue up-to-date. Price £17.50 including postage and packing and first issue of newsletter.

> Published by CERCI Communications,
> 19, Store Street,
> London WC1E 7BT.
> Telephone:071 636 1802

'CPD in the Construction Industry'

'State of the art' paper of latest developments in CPD by the CPD in Construction Group, professional institutions and others. Revised periodically. 20pp A4. Price £3.00 including postage and packing.

> Published by CPD in Construction Group,
> 26, Store Street,

London WC1E 7BT.
Telephone:071 637 0439

'CPDC Newsletter'

Quarterly summary of developments in CPD and review of new distance learning material, courses and publications. 4pp A4. Subscription £4.00 per year.

Published by CPD in Construction Group,
26, Store Street,
London WC1E 7BT.
Telephone: 071 637 0439

'Ensuring Quality in Open Learning'

A code of practice and a series of action guides for producers, deliverers, sponsors and individual learners. A5 ring binder 200pp. Price £9.50.

Published by The Training Agency,
Learning Systems & Access Branch,
St Mary's House, Moorfoot,
Sheffield S1 4PQ.
Telephone:0742 59 4680

Further Education Unit Publications

The FEU issues a series of bulletins and occasional research reports.

'Staff Development for PICKUP - Workshop Materials Manual'

Published 1988.

Publications list obtainable from the Further Education Unit,
Grove House,
2, Orange Street,
London WC2H 7WE.
Telephone:071 321 0433

'Macmillan PICKUP National Training Directory 1991'

Second edition of a two volume directory of 21,000 short work-related courses ranging from half-day to one year part-time on offer throughout the UK. Price £75 plus £2 postage and packing.

Distributed by Globe Book Services Ltd,
Brunel Road,
Houndmills,
Basingstoke,
Hampshire RG21 2XS.
Telephone:0256 29242

'Open Learning in Construction'

Directory of some 600 entries of open learning material for the construction industry. 80pp A5. Free on request.

A Choice of Events:

Events with the following titles have been suggested or are being run by respondents. They are in no particular order. The list does not include a host of titles covering technical subjects such as 'maintenance and repair of brickwork', 'development briefs' and, 'energy conservation'.

Information Technology
Public Enquiries
Report Writing
Induction
Computer Appreciation
Financial Analysis
Addressing Meetings
Team Work
Delegation
Motivation
Meeting the Media
SMM7
QA
Team Building
Managing the Design & Process
Programming a Project
Communication
Specifications — performance
Building Regulations
Arbitration
Party Wall Legislation
Planning Law
Technical Updates
Understanding Accounts
Professional Indemnity
Marketing
Learning and Mentoring
Spreadsheets
Materials Up-Date
Site Visits
Health & Safety
Finance for the non-financial

Word Processing
Telephone Enquiries
Presentations
Disciplinary Procedures
Equal Opportunity Legislation
Programme Logic
Chairing a Meeting
Leadership Style
Supervision
New Legislation
Coordinated Project Information
New and Amended Contracts
Time Management
Interpersonal Skills
Computer Aided Design
Management Skills
Specifications — writing
Refurbishment
Building Standards
Codes of Practice
Technical Innovation
Testing Methods
Running a Practice
Claims
Team Coordination
Project Management
PC Introduction
Controlling Subcontractors
Interviewing
1992
R & D

APPENDICES

Acknowledgements

The following are thanked for the help and time which they gave to the project:

Ben Walters, Costain Group

Malcolm Morley, Kyle Stewart

J M Kane, Bovis

Dudley Hewson, Pascall & Watson

R Murphy, Symonds

Paul Trott, Cheltenham & Gloucester Building Society

W R Ainsworth, Ainsworth Spark Associates

Nigel Lloyd, Transportation Planning Association

G A Mees, Scottish Homes (North Practice)

J M Pitts, John German Estate Office

D O Wall, Hereford & Worcester County Council

R J L Whittaker, Vincent & Gorbing

David Carr, Edward Erdman

D K Atkinson, Lloyds Bank

Roger Chantrelle, Ove Arup Partnership

R Bilbie, c/o Feilden & Mawson

M A Gallacher, London Borough of Barnet

M Warren, John Mowlem & Company

P J Grubb, Conder Structures

Mr P Brooks, Miller Group

Tarmac Construction

Andrew Flood, Thurrock Borough Council

D Brown, Wandsworth Borough Council

Norman Roberts, Kingston Polytechnic

Alan Foster, Sir Robert McAlpine & Sons

Mark Payne, Wimpey Group Services

A Marr, John Laing Developments

Chris Brett, Barton Willmore Planning Partnership

John Henderson, Broadway Malyan

James Brooks-Fisher, BDP

Bob Savage, Phil Turner & Paula Moran Hampshire County Council

Brian Barnes, Higgs & Hill

J A Hayes, R Mansell

and Carmel Leahy CERCI secretary for her work on the draft

CPD in Construction Group

President   **Lord Chilver of Cranfield FRS**

Chairman   **Philip D B Groves RIBA DL**

Secretary   **Dennis A Neale OBE MC Hon FCIOB Hon AIC FBIM**

26 Store Street London WC1E 7BT
Tel: 071 - 637 0439

The CPD in Construction Group was formed in 1980 to bring together the efforts of the participating bodies in the field of CPD and by so doing to strengthen them individually and collectively. It now works in collaboration with the Construction Industry Council.

Membership

The bodies currently in membership of the Group are:

Members

Chartered Institute of Building

Chartered Institution of Building Services Engineers

Institution of Civil Engineers

Institution of Structural Engineers

Royal Institute of British Architects

Royal Institution of Chartered Surveyors

Royal Town Planning Institute

Associate Members

Architects' Registration Council of the United Kingdom

Architects & Surveyors Institute

British Institute of Architectural Technicians

Building Centre Trust

Building Research Establishment

Incorporated Association of Architects and Surveyors

Institute of Maintenance and Building Management

Institution of Civil Engineering Surveyors

Observers

Representatives of:

Department of Education and Science (PICKUP)

Department of Employment (Training Agency)

Department of the Environment

Activities

In its eleven years' existence the CPDC Group has:

Acted as an information exchange about and given encouragement to the development of CPD in the constituent professional institutions and others.

Provided information about CPD activities in other professions e.g. accountants, general medical practitioners, pharmacists, and veterinary surgeons.

Brought pressure to bear on the Government for more support for CPD.

Established links with universities, polytechnics, colleges and other bodies engaged in providing facilities for CPD.

Held conferences and seminars to propagate ideas on CPD.

Provided Information Membership for course providers and others who wish to keep in touch with developments in CPD in the construction industry.

Publications

The following are published by the Group:

CPDC Newsletter

Quarterly issue about CPD developments, new distance learning material and publications. Annual subscription for four issues £4.00.

'State of the art' paper on CPD in the Construction Industry

Published twice yearly. £3.00 per issue.

Occasional Papers

Published from time to time about developments relating to CPD e.g 'Continual Vocational Training in the EC'.

Bibliography for CPD Officers

Shortlist of reference publications considered desirable for anyone responsible for the administration or provision of CPD.

Distance Learning Material

The following is available on sale from the Group:

Audio-visual packages in the 'Better Building' series:

'Commissioning of Buildings'

'Energy Effectiveness'

'Contract Procedures'

'Building Defects'

'Performance Specifications'

'Interaction of Structure and Cladding'

Each package includes an introductory video and supporting printed material. Price £45.00 each including UK postage and packaging plus £6.75 VAT. Two or more £40.00 each plus £6.00 VAT.

CPD Kit — 'Managing Professional Teamwork in the Construction Industry'

The Kit is a total of 248 pages in a ring binder, price £35.00 including UK postage and packing plus £5.25 VAT.

Current Projects

As a companion to this Guide the Group is producing a video about CPD which will be available early in 1991.

A policy statement for the future development of CPD has been prepared.